December 98'

Merry Christmas, Ed —

my favorite golfer!

Love,

~om

Golf is a game whose aim it to hit a very small
ball into an even smaller hole, with weapons
singularly ill-designed for the purpose.

*Sir Winston Churchill*

# The Golf Book

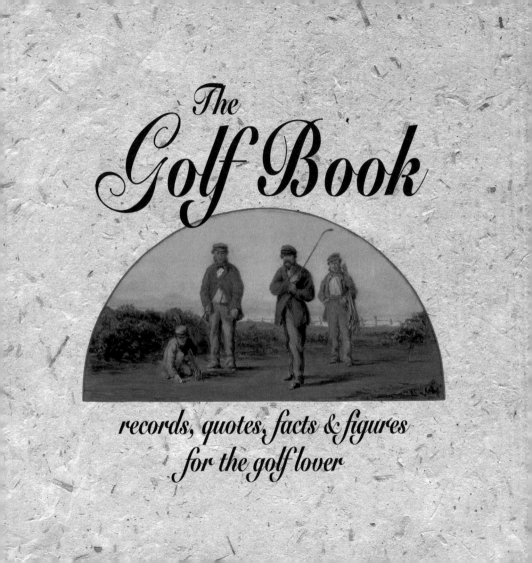

*records, quotes, facts & figures for the golf lover*

## Men's Golf

A form of golf was played in China 1800 years ago, while the French, Dutch and Belgians played something resembling the sport in the middle ages. However, Scotland is generally considered to be the home of golf, and the world's first golf club, the Honourable Company of Edinburgh Golfers, was founded in 1744.

The four majors in men's golf are:

British Open (first held 1860)
US Open (first held 1895)
US Masters (first held in 1934)
US PGA Championship (first held 1916)

Other important tournaments include the Ryder Cup, the World Cup and the Dunhill Cup as well as many amateur competitions.

Winner of the 1976 Dutch Open, at 19 years and 121 days, Severiano Ballesteros of Spain was the youngest winner on the European Tour. The oldest winner was Sandy Herd at 58 in 1926. The youngest winner on the American Tour was John McDermott at 19 years and 10 months in 1911, whilst the oldest was 52 year old Sam Snead in 1965.

Golf is deceptively simple, endlessly complicated.
A child can play it well and a grown man can never master it.
It is almost a science, yet a puzzle with no answer.

*Arnold Palmer*

All games are silly, but golf, if you look at it dispassionately,.
goes to extremes.

*Peter Alliss*

A golf course is the epitome of all that is purely transitory
in the universe, a space not to dwell in, but to get over
as quickly as possible.

*Jean Giraudoux*

# Golfing Records

Course ............................................................ Date ............................

Competition ................................................................................

Players ............................................................................................

............................................................................................

| Hole | Yards | Par | Self | Opponent |
|------|-------|-----|------|----------|
| 1    |       |     |      |          |
| 2    |       |     |      |          |
| 3    |       |     |      |          |
| 4    |       |     |      |          |
| 5    |       |     |      |          |
| 6    |       |     |      |          |
| 7    |       |     |      |          |
| 8    |       |     |      |          |
| 9    |       |     |      |          |
| Out  |       |     |      |          |

| Hole | Yards | Par | Self | Opponent |
|------|-------|-----|------|----------|
| 10   |       |     |      |          |
| 11   |       |     |      |          |
| 12   |       |     |      |          |
| 13   |       |     |      |          |
| 14   |       |     |      |          |
| 15   |       |     |      |          |
| 16   |       |     |      |          |
| 17   |       |     |      |          |
| 18   |       |     |      |          |
| In   |       |     |      |          |
| Out  |       |     |      |          |
| Total |      |     |      |          |
| Handicap |   |     |      |          |
| Net Score |  |     |      |          |

Competitor's
Signature ............................................................

Marker's
Signature ............................................................

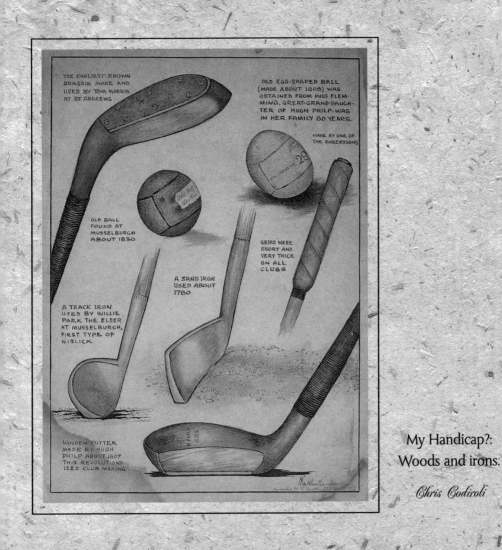

THE EARLIEST KNOWN BRASSIE MADE AND USED BY TOM MORRIS AT ST ANDREWS

OLD EGG-SHAPED BALL (MADE ABOUT 1808) WAS OBTAINED FROM MISS FLEMMING, GREAT-GRAND-DAUGHTER OF HUGH PHILP. WAS IN HER FAMILY 80 YEARS.

MADE BY ONE OF THE ROBERTSONS

OLD BALL FOUND AT MUSSELBURGH ABOUT 1830

GRIPS WERE SHORT AND VERY THICK ON ALL CLUBS

A SAND IRON USED ABOUT 1780

A TRACK IRON USED BY WILLIE PARK THE ELDER AT MUSSELBURGH, FIRST TYPE OF NIBLICK

WOODEN PUTTER MADE BY HUGH PHILP ABOUT 1807 THIS REVOLUTION-IZED CLUB MAKING

My Handicap?:
Woods and irons.

*Chris Codiroli*

I never pray on the golf course. Actually, the Lord answers my
prayers everywhere except on the course.

*Billy Graham*

He's hit it fat. … It will probably be short. …
It just hit the front edge of the green. … It's got no chance. …
It's rolling but it will stop. … It's rolling toward the cup. …
Well, I'll be damned!

*Jimmy Demaret (commentating at the World Championship in 1953
on Lew Worsham's winning wedge shot)*

Golf is like a love affair. If you don't take it seriously,
it's no fun; if you do take it seriously, it breaks your heart.

*Arnold Daly*

# *Golfing Records*

Course .................................................... Date ....................

Competition ....................................................

Players ....................................................

....................................................

| Hole | Yards | Par | Self | Opponent |
|------|-------|-----|------|----------|
| 1 | | | | |
| 2 | | | | |
| 3 | | | | |
| 4 | | | | |
| 5 | | | | |
| 6 | | | | |
| 7 | | | | |
| 8 | | | | |
| 9 | | | | |
| Out | | | | |

| Hole | Yards | Par | Self | Opponent |
|------|-------|-----|------|----------|
| 10 | | | | |
| 11 | | | | |
| 12 | | | | |
| 13 | | | | |
| 14 | | | | |
| 15 | | | | |
| 16 | | | | |
| 17 | | | | |
| 18 | | | | |
| In | | | | |
| Out | | | | |
| Total | | | | |
| Handicap | | | | |
| Net Score | | | | |

Competitor's
Signature ....................................................

Marker's
Signature ....................................................

The right way to play golf is to go
up and hit the bloody thing.

*George Duncan*

My game is so bad I gotta hire three caddies –
one to walk the left rough, one for the right rough,
and one down the middle.
And the one in the middle doesn't have much to do.

*Dave Hill*

The person I fear most in the last two rounds is myself.

*Tom Watson (at the US Open)*

Golf is a game in which a ball – one and a half inches
in diameter – is placed on a ball – 8,000 miles in diameter.
The object being to hit the small ball, but not the larger.

*John Cunningham*

# Facts & Figures

## Leading Annual Money Winners Europe (1980 - 1994)

|  |  |  |
|------|--------|--------|
| 1980 | Greg Norman (Aus) | £74,829 |
| 1981 | Bernard Langer (FRG) | £95,991 |
| 1982 | Sandy Lyle (UK) | £86,141 |
| 1983 | Nick Faldo (UK) | £140,761 |
| 1984 | Bernard Langer (FRG) | £160,883 |
| 1985 | Sandy Lyle (UK) | £199,020 |
| 1986 | Severiano Ballesteros (Spa) | £259,275 |
| 1987 | Ian Woosnam (UK) | £439,075 |
| 1988 | Severiano Ballesteros (Spa) | £502,000 |
| 1989 | Ronan Rafferty (Ire) | £465,981 |
| 1990 | Ian Woosnam (UK) | £574,166 |
| 1991 | Severiano Ballesteros (Spa) | £545,353 |
| 1992 | Nick Faldo (UK) | £708,522 |
| 1993 | Colin Montgomerie (UK) | £613,682 |
| 1994 | Colin Montgomerie (UK) | £762,719 |

## Leading Annual Money Winners US (1980 - 1994)

|  |  |  |
|------|--------|--------|
| 1980 | Tom Watson (USA) | $530,808 |
| 1981 | Tom Kite (USA) | $375,698 |
| 1982 | Craig Stadler (USA) | $446,462 |
| 1983 | Hal Sutton (USA) | $426,668 |
| 1984 | Tom Watson (USA) | $476,260 |
| 1985 | Curtis Strange (USA) | $542,321 |
| 1986 | Greg Norman (Aus) | $653,296 |
| 1987 | Curtis Strange (USA) | $925,941 |
| 1988 | Curtis Strange (USA) | $1,147,644 |
| 1989 | Tom Kite (USA) | $1,395,278 |
| 1990 | Greg Norman (Aus) | $1,165,477 |
| 1991 | Corey Pavin (USA) | $979,430 |
| 1992 | Fred Couples (USA) | $1,344,188 |
| 1993 | Nick Price (Zim) | $1,478,557 |
| 1994 | Nick Price (Zim) | $1,499,927 |

Ah well. If we hit it perfect
every day, everybody else
would quit.

*Lee Trevino to Tom Watson*

# Golfing Records

Course ............................................................ Date ....................

Competition ....................................................................

Players ....................................................................

....................................................................

| Hole | Yards | Par | Self | Opponent |
|------|-------|-----|------|----------|
| 1 | | | | |
| 2 | | | | |
| 3 | | | | |
| 4 | | | | |
| 5 | | | | |
| 6 | | | | |
| 7 | | | | |
| 8 | | | | |
| 9 | | | | |
| Out | | | | |

| Hole | Yards | Par | Self | Opponent |
|------|-------|-----|------|----------|
| 10 | | | | |
| 11 | | | | |
| 12 | | | | |
| 13 | | | | |
| 14 | | | | |
| 15 | | | | |
| 16 | | | | |
| 17 | | | | |
| 18 | | | | |
| In | | | | |
| Out | | | | |
| Total | | | | |
| Handicap | | | | |
| Net Score | | | | |

Competitor's
Signature ....................................................................

Marker's
Signature ....................................................................

# Golfing Records

Course ........................................................ Date ........................................

Competition ............................................................................................

Players ........................................................................................................

........................................................................................................

| Hole | Yards | Par | Self | Opponent |
|------|-------|-----|------|----------|
| 1 | | | | |
| 2 | | | | |
| 3 | | | | |
| 4 | | | | |
| 5 | | | | |
| 6 | | | | |
| 7 | | | | |
| 8 | | | | |
| 9 | | | | |
| Out | | | | |

| Hole | Yards | Par | Self | Opponent |
|------|-------|-----|------|----------|
| 10 | | | | |
| 11 | | | | |
| 12 | | | | |
| 13 | | | | |
| 14 | | | | |
| 15 | | | | |
| 16 | | | | |
| 17 | | | | |
| 18 | | | | |
| In | | | | |
| Out | | | | |
| Total | | | | |
| Handicap | | | | |
| Net Score | | | | |

Competitor's
Signature ........................................

Marker's
Signature ........................................

Hole-in-One: An occurrence in which a ball is hit directly from the tee into the hole on a single shot by a golfer playing alone.

*Henry Beard & Roy McKie*

I have found, in my own matches, that if you just keep throwing consistent, unvarying bogeys and double bogeys at your opponents, they will crack up sooner or later from the pressure.

*Rex Lardner*

One reason golf is such an exasperating game is that a thing learned is so easily forgotten and we find ourselves struggling year after year with faults we had discovered and corrected time and time again.

*Bobby Jones*

The difference between learning to play golf and learning to drive
a car is that in golf you never hit anything.

*Anon*

You hit the ball and if it doesn't go far enough you just hit it again,
and if that doesn't work, you hit it again, and so on.

*Robert Robinson*

Anytime you get the urge to golf, instead take 18 minutes and
beat your head against a good solid wall! This is guaranteed to
duplicate to a tee the physical and emotional beating you would
have suffered playing a round of golf. If 18 minutes aren't enough,
go for 27 or 36 – whatever feels right.

*Mark Oman*

Most golfers
prepare for disaster.
A good golfer
prepares for success.

*Bob Toski*

## The British Open

The Open first took place at Prestwick on 17 October 1860. Eight competitors took part and the winner, Willy Park senior, won a Championship belt.

Since 1872, the Open has been played over seaside links, and the champion is awarded a silver claret jug. Today, the competition is played over 72 holes.

Prize money was introduced in 1863 and totalled £10.00. In 1995, the total had risen to £1,250,000.00.

The lowest four-round total was scored by Greg Norman in 1993 taking just 267.

At 46, Tom Morris Snr was the oldest player to win the Open (1867). Just one year after, Tom Morris Jr was the youngest to win the competition, aged 17!

## The Winners (1975-1995)

| Year | Winner | Score |
|------|--------|-------|
| 1975 | Tom Watson (USA) | 279* |
| 1976 | Johnny Miller (USA) | 279 |
| 1977 | Tom Watson (USA) | 268 |
| 1978 | Jack Nicklaus (USA) | 281 |
| 1979 | Severiano Ballesteros (Spa) | 283 |
| 1980 | Tom Watson (USA) | 271 |
| 1981 | Bill Rogers (USA) | 276 |
| 1982 | Tom Watson (USA) | 284 |
| 1983 | Tom Watson (USA) | 275 |
| 1984 | Severiano Ballesteros (Spa) | 276 |
| 1985 | Sandy Lyle (UK) | 282 |
| 1986 | Greg Norman (Aus) | 280 |
| 1987 | Nick Faldo (UK) | 279 |
| 1988 | Severiano Ballesteros (Spa) | 273 |
| 1989 | Mark Calcavecchia (USA) | 275* |
| 1990 | Nick Faldo (UK) | 270 |
| 1991 | Ian Baker-Finch (Aus) | 272 |
| 1992 | Nick Faldo (UK) | 272 |
| 1993 | Greg Norman (Aus) | 267 |
| 1994 | Nick Price (Zim) | 268 |
| 1995 | John Daly (USA) | 282* |

* After play-off

# Golfing Records

Course ..................................................... Date .....................

Competition ...................................................................

Players ...................................................................

...................................................................

| Hole | Yards | Par | Self | Opponent |
|------|-------|-----|------|----------|
| 1 | | | | |
| 2 | | | | |
| 3 | | | | |
| 4 | | | | |
| 5 | | | | |
| 6 | | | | |
| 7 | | | | |
| 8 | | | | |
| 9 | | | | |
| Out | | | | |

| Hole | Yards | Par | Self | Opponent |
|------|-------|-----|------|----------|
| 10 | | | | |
| 11 | | | | |
| 12 | | | | |
| 13 | | | | |
| 14 | | | | |
| 15 | | | | |
| 16 | | | | |
| 17 | | | | |
| 18 | | | | |
| In | | | | |
| Out | | | | |
| Total | | | | |
| Handicap | | | | |
| Net Score | | | | |

Competitor's
Signature ...........................................

Marker's
Signature ...........................................

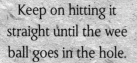

Keep on hitting it
straight until the wee
ball goes in the hole.

*James Braid*

PHILOSOPHER (*eight down to bogey*). "Anyway I don't suppose for one moment the cup is real silver."

My golf swing is like ironing a shirt.  You get one side smoothed out,
turn it over and there is a big wrinkle on the other side.
You iron that side, turn it over and there's another wrinkle.

*Tom Watson*

I still swing the way I used to, but when I look up the ball is going
in a different direction.

*Lee Trevino*

As of this writing, there are approximately 2,450 reasons
why a person hits a rotten shot, and more are being
discovered every day.

*Jay Cronley*

# *Golfing Records*

Course .................................................... Date ....................

Competition ....................................................

Players ....................................................

....................................................

| Hole | Yards | Par | Self | Opponent |
|------|-------|-----|------|----------|
| 1 | | | | |
| 2 | | | | |
| 3 | | | | |
| 4 | | | | |
| 5 | | | | |
| 6 | | | | |
| 7 | | | | |
| 8 | | | | |
| 9 | | | | |
| Out | | | | |

| Hole | Yards | Par | Self | Opponent |
|------|-------|-----|------|----------|
| 10 | | | | |
| 11 | | | | |
| 12 | | | | |
| 13 | | | | |
| 14 | | | | |
| 15 | | | | |
| 16 | | | | |
| 17 | | | | |
| 18 | | | | |
| In | | | | |
| Out | | | | |
| Total | | | | |
| Handicap | | | | |
| Net Score | | | | |

Competitor's
Signature ....................................................

Marker's
Signature ....................................................

When ground rules permit a golfer to improve his lie,
he can either move his ball or change the story
about his score.

*Anon*

Anytime a golfer hits a ball perfectly straight with a big club
it is, in my view, a fluke.

*Jack Nicklaus*

Suffering – ! I've got a hen back home in Charlotte that can
lay an egg further than that!

*Clayton Heafner (missing a 3 inch putt to lose the
Oakland Open by one shot)*

# Golfing Records

Course ............................................................ Date ....................

Competition ............................................................................

Players ....................................................................................

....................................................................................

| Hole | Yards | Par | Self | Opponent |
|------|-------|-----|------|----------|
| 1 | | | | |
| 2 | | | | |
| 3 | | | | |
| 4 | | | | |
| 5 | | | | |
| 6 | | | | |
| 7 | | | | |
| 8 | | | | |
| 9 | | | | |
| Out | | | | |

| Hole | Yards | Par | Self | Opponent |
|------|-------|-----|------|----------|
| 10 | | | | |
| 11 | | | | |
| 12 | | | | |
| 13 | | | | |
| 14 | | | | |
| 15 | | | | |
| 16 | | | | |
| 17 | | | | |
| 18 | | | | |
| In | | | | |
| Out | | | | |
| Total | | | | |
| Handicap | | | | |
| Net Score | | | | |

Competitor's
Signature ..............................................

Marker's
Signature ..............................................

Real golfers don't cry when they line up their fourth putt.

*Karen Hurwitz*

I'd like to see the fairways more narrow. Then everybody would have to play from the rough, not just me.

*Severiano Ballesteros*

Thou shalt not use profanity; thou shalt not covet thy neighbour's putter; thou shalt not steal thy neighbour's ball; thou shalt not bear false witness in the final tally.

*Ground Rules:*
*Clergyman's Golf Tournament, Grand Rapids*

Through years of experience I have found that air offers less resistance than dirt.

*Jack Nicklaus explaining why he tees up the ball so high*

## The US Open

The US Open was first played at Newport, Rhode Island on a 9-hole course on 4th November 1895.

The winner was English-born Horace Rawlins with a score of 173, for which he won $150.00 (the total prize money came to $335.00). In 1995, total prize money collected came to $2 million.

With the exception of the years between 1895 & 1897 the competition has been played over 72 holes.

With a score of 272 in '80, Jack Nicklaus notched up the lowest four-round total.

At 43, Raymond Floyd was the oldest player to win the US Open (1986).

In 1911, at 19, John McDermott was the youngest to win the tournament.

## The Winners (1975–1995)

| 1975 | Lou Graham (USA) | 287 |
|------|------------------|-----|
| 1976 | Jerry Pate (USA) | 277 |
| 1977 | Hubert Green (USA) | 278 |
| 1978 | Andy North (USA) | 285 |
| 1979 | Hale Urwin (USA) | 284 |
| 1980 | Jack Nicklaus (USA) | 272 |
| 1981 | David Graham (Aus) | 273 |
| 1982 | Tom Watson (USA) | 282 |
| 1983 | Larry Nelson (USA) | 280 |
| 1984 | Fuzzy Zoeller (USA) | 276* |
| 1985 | Andy North (USA) | 279 |
| 1986 | Raymond Floyd (USA) | 279 |
| 1987 | Scott Simpson (USA) | 277 |
| 1988 | Curtis Strange (USA) | 278 |
| 1989 | Curtis Strange (USA) | 278 |
| 1990 | Hale Urwin (USA) | 280* |
| 1991 | Payne Stewart (USA) | 282* |
| 1992 | Tom Kite (USA) | 285 |
| 1993 | Lee Janzen (USA) | 272 |
| 1994 | Ernie Els (SAf) | 279* |
| 1995 | Corey Pavin (USA) | 280 |

* After play-off

Golf is a good walk spoiled.
*Mark Twain*

# Golfing Records

Course .................................................... Date ....................

Competition ..............................................................

Players .....................................................................

.....................................................................

| Hole | Yards | Par | Self | Opponent |
|------|-------|-----|------|----------|
| 1 | | | | |
| 2 | | | | |
| 3 | | | | |
| 4 | | | | |
| 5 | | | | |
| 6 | | | | |
| 7 | | | | |
| 8 | | | | |
| 9 | | | | |
| Out | | | | |

| Hole | Yards | Par | Self | Opponent |
|------|-------|-----|------|----------|
| 10 | | | | |
| 11 | | | | |
| 12 | | | | |
| 13 | | | | |
| 14 | | | | |
| 15 | | | | |
| 16 | | | | |
| 17 | | | | |
| 18 | | | | |
| In | | | | |
| Out | | | | |
| Total | | | | |
| Handicap | | | | |
| Net Score | | | | |

Competitor's
Signature ....................................................

Marker's
Signature ....................................................

No man has mastered golf until he has realised that his good shots
are accidents and his bad shots good exercise.

*Eugene R Black*

The nice thing about these [golf] books is that they usually cancel
each other out.  One book tells you to keep your eye on the ball;
the next says not to bother.  Personally, in the crowd I play with,
a better idea is to keep your eye on your partner.

*Jim Murray*

Everybody has two swings – a beautiful practice swing
and a choked-up one with which they hit the ball.
So it wouldn't do either of us a damned bit of good
to look at your practice swing.

*Ed Furgol*

A golf game doesn't end
until the last putt drops.

*Cary Middlecoff*

Golf appeals to the idiot in us and the child . . .
Just how childlike golf players become is proven by their frequent
inability to count past five.

*John Updike*

I remember being upset once and telling my Dad I wasn't following
through right, and he replied, 'Nancy, it doesn't make any difference
to a ball what you do after you hit it.'

*Nancy Lopez*

Well, in plain old English, I'm driving it bad, chipping bad,
putting bad, and not scoring at all.  Other than that, and the
fact I got up this morning, I guess everything's okay.

*Bob Wynn*

## The US Masters

The US Masters, first introduced in 1934, was the brain child of the legendary golfer Bobby Jones, who also designed the course at Augusta, Georgia where the tournament is annually held. The first winner was Horton Smith with a score of 284.

Entry is by invitation only and the winner earns the coveted green jacket.

The competition is played over 72 holes of stroke-play.

Scoring 271 in 1965 and 1976 respectively, Jack Nicklaus and Raymond Floyd take the credit for the lowest four-round totals.

His win in 1986 made Jack Nicklaus, at 46, the oldest winner yet of the US Masters, while in 1980, Seve Ballesteros was the youngest to win – at 23.

## The Winners (1975–1995)

| 1975 | Jack Nicklaus (USA) | 276 |
| 1976 | Raymond Floyd (USA) | 271 |
| 1977 | Tom Watson (USA) | 276 |
| 1978 | Gary Player (SAf) | 277 |
| 1979 | Fuzzy Zoeller (USA) | 280* |
| 1980 | Severiano Ballesteros (Spa) | 275 |
| 1981 | Tom Watson (USA) | 280 |
| 1982 | Craig Stadler (USA) | 284* |
| 1983 | Severiano Ballesteros (Spa) | 280 |
| 1984 | Ben Crenshaw (USA) | 277 |
| 1985 | Bernhard Langer (FRG) | 282 |
| 1986 | Jack Nicklaus (USA) | 279 |
| 1987 | Larry Mize (USA) | 285* |
| 1988 | Sandy Lyle (UK) | 281 |
| 1989 | Nick Faldo (UK) | 283* |
| 1990 | Nick Faldo (UK) | 278* |
| 1991 | Ian Woosnam (UK) | 277 |
| 1992 | Fred Couples (USA) | 275 |
| 1993 | Bernard Langer (Ger) | 277 |
| 1994 | José Maria Olazábal (Spa) | 279 |
| 1995 | Ben Crenshaw (USA) | 274 |

* After play-off

Course .......................................................... Date ..........................................

Competition ....................................................................................................

Players ...............................................  ...............................................

...............................................  ...............................................

| Hole | Yards | Par | Self | Opponent |
|------|-------|-----|------|----------|
| 1 | | | | |
| 2 | | | | |
| 3 | | | | |
| 4 | | | | |
| 5 | | | | |
| 6 | | | | |
| 7 | | | | |
| 8 | | | | |
| 9 | | | | |
| Out | | | | |

| Hole | Yards | Par | Self | Opponent |
|------|-------|-----|------|----------|
| 10 | | | | |
| 11 | | | | |
| 12 | | | | |
| 13 | | | | |
| 14 | | | | |
| 15 | | | | |
| 16 | | | | |
| 17 | | | | |
| 18 | | | | |
| In | | | | |
| Out | | | | |
| Total | | | | |
| Handicap | | | | |
| Net Score | | | | |

Competitor's
Signature ..........................................................

Marker's
Signature ..........................................................

You get to know more of the character of a man in a round of golf than you can get to know in six months with only political experience.

*David Lloyd George*

When he gets the ball into a tough place, that's when he's most relaxed. I think it's because he has so much experience at it.

*Don Christopher (Jack Lemon's caddie)*

My caddie had the best answer to that – 'Just to let the other one know it can be replaced.'

*Larry Nelson explaining why he carried two putters*

Golf is a fickle game, and must
be wooed to be won.

*Willy Park Jr*

# Golfing Records

Course .................................................. Date ..........................

Competition ..................................................................

Players .........................................................................

.........................................................................

| Hole | Yards | Par | Self | Opponent |
|------|-------|-----|------|----------|
| 1 | | | | |
| 2 | | | | |
| 3 | | | | |
| 4 | | | | |
| 5 | | | | |
| 6 | | | | |
| 7 | | | | |
| 8 | | | | |
| 9 | | | | |
| Out | | | | |

| Hole | Yards | Par | Self | Opponent |
|------|-------|-----|------|----------|
| 10 | | | | |
| 11 | | | | |
| 12 | | | | |
| 13 | | | | |
| 14 | | | | |
| 15 | | | | |
| 16 | | | | |
| 17 | | | | |
| 18 | | | | |
| In | | | | |
| Out | | | | |
| Total | | | | |
| Handicap | | | | |
| Net Score | | | | |

Competitor's
Signature ..................................................

Marker's
Signature ..................................................

Over the years, I've studied habits of golfers. I know what to look for. Watch their eyes. Fear shows up when there is an enlargement of the pupils. Big pupils lead to big scores.

*Sam Snead*

If a ball comes to rest in dangerous proximity to a hippopotamus or crocodile, another ball may be dropped at a safe distance, no nearer the hole, without penalty.

*Local Rule: Nyanza Club, British East Africa in the 1950s*

Always throw clubs ahead of you. That way you don't have to waste energy going back to pick them up.

*Tommy Bolt*

If ah didn't have these ah'd
hit it twenty yards further.

*Babe Didrikson Zaharias
(referring to her breasts)*

## The US PGA Championship

The US PGA Championship was first
played in 1916 at Siwanoy. The winner
was Jim Barnes, scoring 1 up.

It was held as a match-play event until
1958, when it became a stroke-play
competition over four rounds.

Entry is based on qualification from the
Professional Golfers Association tour and
the competition is the least publicised of
the four majors.

The lowest four-round total was scored in
1964 by Bobby Nichols, who completed in
271.

The oldest winner of the Championship
was Julius Boros in 1968 at 48.

The youngest winner was Gene Sarazen in
1922 when he was just 20 years old.

## The Winners (1975-1995)

| Year | Winner | Score |
|------|--------|-------|
| 1975 | Jack Nicklaus (USA) | 276 |
| 1976 | Dave Stockton (USA) | 281 |
| 1977 | Lanny Wadkins (USA) | 282* |
| 1978 | John Mahaffey (USA) | 276* |
| 1979 | David Graham (Aus) | 272* |
| 1980 | Jack Nicklaus (USA) | 274 |
| 1981 | Larry Nelson (USA) | 273 |
| 1982 | Raymond Floyd (USA) | 272 |
| 1983 | Hal Sutton (USA) | 274 |
| 1984 | Lee Trevino (USA) | 273 |
| 1985 | Hubert Green (USA) | 278 |
| 1986 | Bob Tway (USA) | 276 |
| 1987 | Larry Nelson (USA) | 287* |
| 1988 | Jeff Sluman (USA) | 272 |
| 1989 | Payne Stewart (USA) | 276 |
| 1990 | Wayne Grady (Aus) | 282 |
| 1991 | John Daly (USA) | 276 |
| 1992 | Nick Price (Zim) | 278 |
| 1993 | Paul Azinger (USA) | 272* |
| 1994 | Nick Price (Zim) | 269 |
| 1995 | Steve Elkington (Aus) | 267* |

* After play-off

He enjoys that perfect peace, that peace beyond all
understanding, which comes at its maximum only to
the man who has given up golf.

*P G Wodehouse*

If the tree is skinny, aim right at it. A peculiarity of golf is that what
you aim at you generally miss, . . . the success of the shot depending
mainly, of course, on your definition of 'skinny.'

*Rex Lardner*

The little white ball won't move until you've hit it, and there's
nothing you can do after it has gone.

*Babe Didrikson Zaharias*

# Golfing Records

Course ........................................................... Date ...................................

Competition ...........................................................................................

Players ...........................................................................................

...........................................................................................

| Hole | Yards | Par | Self | Opponent |
|------|-------|-----|------|----------|
| 1 | | | | |
| 2 | | | | |
| 3 | | | | |
| 4 | | | | |
| 5 | | | | |
| 6 | | | | |
| 7 | | | | |
| 8 | | | | |
| 9 | | | | |
| Out | | | | |

| Hole | Yards | Par | Self | Opponent |
|------|-------|-----|------|----------|
| 10 | | | | |
| 11 | | | | |
| 12 | | | | |
| 13 | | | | |
| 14 | | | | |
| 15 | | | | |
| 16 | | | | |
| 17 | | | | |
| 18 | | | | |
| In | | | | |
| Out | | | | |
| Total | | | | |
| Handicap | | | | |
| Net Score | | | | |

Competitor's
Signature ...........................................................

Marker's
Signature ...........................................................

# Golfing Records

Course .................................................... Date ....................................

Competition ....................................................................................

Players ....................................................................................

....................................................................................

| Hole | Yards | Par | Self | Opponent |
|------|-------|-----|------|----------|
| 1 | | | | |
| 2 | | | | |
| 3 | | | | |
| 4 | | | | |
| 5 | | | | |
| 6 | | | | |
| 7 | | | | |
| 8 | | | | |
| 9 | | | | |
| Out | | | | |

| Hole | Yards | Par | Self | Opponent |
|------|-------|-----|------|----------|
| 10 | | | | |
| 11 | | | | |
| 12 | | | | |
| 13 | | | | |
| 14 | | | | |
| 15 | | | | |
| 16 | | | | |
| 17 | | | | |
| 18 | | | | |
| In | | | | |
| Out | | | | |
| Total | | | | |
| Handicap | | | | |
| Net Score | | | | |

Competitor's
Signature ....................................

Marker's
Signature ....................................

HEART-BROKEN COMPETITOR (*who has missed a quick putt*). "Now wouldn't you call that provoking?"
CADDIE. "Well, Miss, that's a word I don't use meself."

It's funny, but the more I practice, the luckier I become.

*Gary Player*

## Women's Golf

The Women's Professional Golf Association (WPGA) was formed in the USA in 1944 and was reformed in 1948 as the Ladies' Professional Golf Association (LPGA).

The four majors in US women's golf are:

US Women's Open (first held 1946)
LPGA Championship (first held 1955)
Nabisco Dinah Shore (major status from 1983)
Du Maurier Classic (major status from 1979)

Mickey Wright has had the most wins since the formation of the US LPGA in 1950: she has won the US Women's Open and the LPGA Championship four times each (1958-64).

The British Women's Open Championship was first contested in 1976. It is an annual stroke-play competition.

The Women's PGA European Tour was formed in 1979.

You've just one problem. You stand too close to the ball –
after you've hit it.

*Sam Snead (to a pupil)*

Golf acts as a corrective against sinful pride. I attribute the insane
arrogance of the later Roman emperors almost entirely to the fact
that, never having played golf, they never knew that strange
chastening humility which is engendered by a topped chip shot.

*P G Wodehouse*

If you keep shooting par at them, they all crack up
sooner or later.

*Bobby Jones*

My goal this year is basically to find the fairways.

*Lauri Peterson*

# Golfing Records

Course ........................................................... Date ...........................

Competition ...................................................................................

Players ...........................................................................................

...........................................................................................

| Hole | Yards | Par | Self | Opponent |
|------|-------|-----|------|----------|
| 1 | | | | |
| 2 | | | | |
| 3 | | | | |
| 4 | | | | |
| 5 | | | | |
| 6 | | | | |
| 7 | | | | |
| 8 | | | | |
| 9 | | | | |
| Out | | | | |

| Hole | Yards | Par | Self | Opponent |
|------|-------|-----|------|----------|
| 10 | | | | |
| 11 | | | | |
| 12 | | | | |
| 13 | | | | |
| 14 | | | | |
| 15 | | | | |
| 16 | | | | |
| 17 | | | | |
| 18 | | | | |
| In | | | | |
| Out | | | | |
| Total | | | | |
| Handicap | | | | |
| Net Score | | | | |

Competitor's
Signature ...........................................................

Marker's
Signature ...........................................................

President Ford waits until he hits his first drive to know what course he's playing that day.

*Bob Hope*

The golfer has more enemies than any other athlete. He has 14 clubs in his bag, all of them different; 18 holes to play, all of them different, every week; and all around him are sand, trees, grass, water, wind and 143 other players. In addition, the game is fifty percent mental, so his biggest enemy is himself.

*Dan Jenkins*

When they start hitting back at me, it's time to quit.

*Henry Ransom*
*(when a shot rebounded from a cliff and hit him in the stomach)*

All I have against it
is that it takes you
so far from the
clubhouse.

*Eric Linklater*

# Golfing Records

Course ........................................................... Date ........................

Competition ....................................................................................

Players ........................................................................................

........................................................................................

| Hole | Yards | Par | Self | Opponent |
|------|-------|-----|------|----------|
| 1 | | | | |
| 2 | | | | |
| 3 | | | | |
| 4 | | | | |
| 5 | | | | |
| 6 | | | | |
| 7 | | | | |
| 8 | | | | |
| 9 | | | | |
| Out | | | | |

| Hole | Yards | Par | Self | Opponent |
|------|-------|-----|------|----------|
| 10 | | | | |
| 11 | | | | |
| 12 | | | | |
| 13 | | | | |
| 14 | | | | |
| 15 | | | | |
| 16 | | | | |
| 17 | | | | |
| 18 | | | | |
| In | | | | |
| Out | | | | |
| Total | | | | |
| Handicap | | | | |
| Net Score | | | | |

Competitor's
Signature ........................................................

Marker's
Signature ........................................................

He quit playing when I started outdriving him.

*JoAnne Carner (referring to her husband Don)*

The fundamental problem with golf is that every so often,
no matter how lacking you may be in the essential virtues required
of a steady player, the odds are that one day you will hit the ball
straight, hard and out of sight. This is the essential frustration of this
excruciating sport. For when you've done it once, you make the
fundamental error of asking yourself why you can't do it all the time.
The answer to this question is simple: the first time was a fluke.

*Colin Bowles*

Golf is a game in which you yell Fore,
shoot six, and write down five.

*Paul Harvey*

# Facts & Figures

## US LPGA Money Leaders (1980 - 1994)

|  |  |  |
|------|--------|--------|
| 1980 | Beth Daniel (USA) | $231,000 |
| 1981 | Beth Daniel (USA) | $206,978 |
| 1982 | JoAnne Carner (USA) | $310,399 |
| 1983 | JoAnne Carner (USA) | $291,404 |
| 1984 | Betsy King (USA) | $266,771 |
| 1985 | Nancy Lopez (USA) | $416,472 |
| 1986 | Pat Bradley (USA) | $492,021 |
| 1987 | Ayoko Okomoto (Jap) | $466,034 |
| 1988 | Sherru Turner (USA) | $350,851 |
| 1989 | Betsy King (USA) | $654,132 |
| 1990 | Beth Daniel (USA) | $863,578 |
| 1991 | Pat Bradley (USA) | $763,118 |
| 1992 | Dottie Mochrie (USA) | $693,355 |
| 1993 | Betsy King (USA) | $595,992 |
| 1994 | Laura Davies (UK) | $687,201 |

## Womens PGA European Tour Money Leaders (1980 - 1994)

|  |  |  |
|------|--------|--------|
| 1980 | Muriel Thomson (UK) | £8,008 |
| 1981 | Jenny Lee Smith (UK) | £13,519 |
| 1982 | Jenny Lee Smith (UK) | £12,551 |
| 1983 | Beverly Huke (UK) | £9,226 |
| 1984 | Dale Reid (UK) | £28,239 |
| 1985 | Laura Davies (UK) | £21,736 |
| 1986 | Laura Davies (UK) | £37,500 |
| 1987 | Dale Reid (UK) | £53,815 |
| 1988 | Marie-Laure de Lorenzi (Fra) | £99,360 |
| 1989 | Marie-Laure de Lorenzi (Fra) | £77,534 |
| 1990 | Trish Johnson (UK) | £83,403 |
| 1991 | Corinne Dibnah (Aus) | £89,058 |
| 1992 | Laura Davies (UK) | £66,333 |
| 1993 | Karen Lunn (Aus) | £66,266 |
| 1994 | Liselotte Neumann (Swe) | £102,750 |

# Golfing Records

Course .................................................................................................... Date ................................................

Competition ....................................................................................................................................

Players ....................................................................................................................................

....................................................................................................................................

| Hole | Yards | Par | Self | Opponent |
|------|-------|-----|------|----------|
| 1 | | | | |
| 2 | | | | |
| 3 | | | | |
| 4 | | | | |
| 5 | | | | |
| 6 | | | | |
| 7 | | | | |
| 8 | | | | |
| 9 | | | | |
| Out | | | | |

| Hole | Yards | Par | Self | Opponent |
|------|-------|-----|------|----------|
| 10 | | | | |
| 11 | | | | |
| 12 | | | | |
| 13 | | | | |
| 14 | | | | |
| 15 | | | | |
| 16 | | | | |
| 17 | | | | |
| 18 | | | | |
| In | | | | |
| Out | | | | |
| Total | | | | |
| Handicap | | | | |
| Net Score | | | | |

Competitor's
Signature ........................................................

Marker's
Signature ........................................................

There is one
essential only in the
golf swing, the ball
must be hit.

*Sir Walter Simpson*

This edition © Robert Frederick Ltd. 1997
Old Orchard Street, Bath BA1 1JU, England

Printed by Man Sang Envelope Manufacturing Co. Ltd., China

Acknowledgements

Oil Study for Frontispiece of R Clark's 'Golf - A Royal & Ancient Game.'
by Clark Stanton (1823-1894)
Private Collection/Bridgeman Art Library, London

'Copies Golfers', Edwardian Cigarette Cards in an Album
Private Collection/Bridgeman Art Library, London

Golfing at Westward Ho! by Francis Powell Hopkins (1830-1913)
Private Collection/Bridgeman Art Library, London

Portrait of John Whyte Melville of Bennochy and Strathkinness,
Captain of the Club 1823 by Sir Francis Grant (1810-1878)
Royal & Ancient Golf Club, St Andrews/Bridgeman Art Library, London

View of Military Players at St Andrews, late 17th century
English School (17th century), Royal & Ancient Golf Club, St Andrews
© Phaidon Press Ltd/David Cripps/Bridgeman Art Library, London

Cover of Harper's Magazine, april 1898
Lords Gallery, London/Bridgeman Art Library

Ladies Match at Westward Ho! by Francis Powell Hopkins (1830-1913)
Private Collection/Bridgeman Art Library, London

Prince of Wales, later Kind Edward VIII (s & d 1927) by Sir William Orpen (1878-1931)
Royal & Ancient Golf Club, St Andrews/Bridgeman Art Library

'How you can detect your true golfer from the ordinary man in the street'
by William Heath Robinson (1872-1944)
Chris Beetles Ltd, London/Bridgeman Art Library, London

Other images © Robert Frederick Archives